Informal Assessments for
Text Comprehension

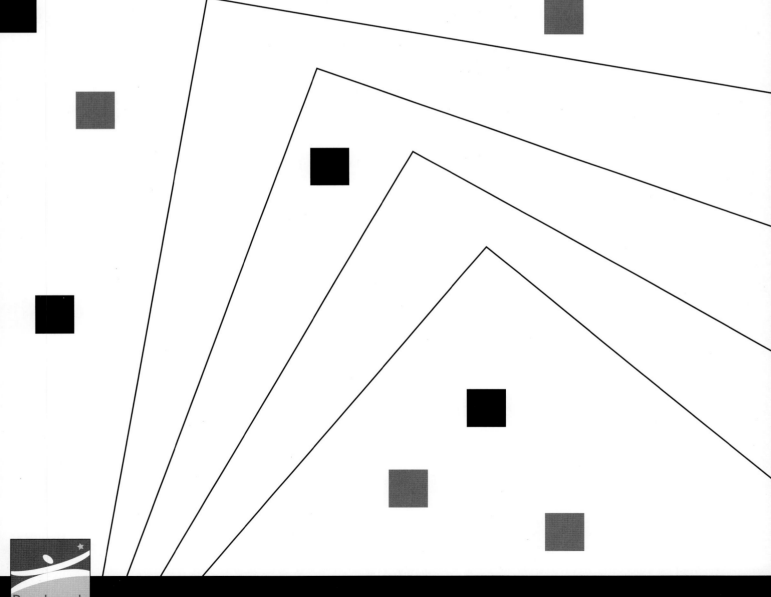

Benchmark
EDUCATION

BENCHMARK EDUCATION COMPANY

Benchmark Education Company
145 Huguenot Street • New Rochelle, NY 10801
www.benchmarkeducation.com

ISBN: 978-1-4509-2882-3

For ordering information, call Toll-Free 1-877-236-2465 or visit our Web site: www.benchmarkeducation.com.

Informal Assessments for Text Comprehension

Table of Contents

Benchmark
EDUCATION
Building Literacy for Life™

Assessment Introduction

Daily teaching goes hand in hand with ongoing assessment and evaluation. The wide variety of reading, writing, spelling, and language assessments provided by Benchmark Education Company enables teachers to:

- obtain multiple perspectives on the literacy growth occurring in their classrooms;
- monitor and reflect on their teaching and students' learning;
- make informed decisions about students' progress and needs;
- select appropriate materials and instructional techniques that match students' current level of development;
- document progress over time through a cumulative portfolio;
- report progress to students, parents, and administrators.

Meaningful, ongoing, and multifaceted observation is the heart of the evaluation process. Since observations must occur in authentic contexts, utilize your small-group reading time to document students' efforts to join discussions; ask and answer questions; react to prompts; contribute ideas for graphic organizers; process text; problem-solve new words; apply targeted skills and strategies, and act out and/or talk, draw, or write about books.

The integration of assessment, teaching, and learning supports effective literacy instruction. Benchmark Education Company provides teachers with the tools for understanding and documenting literacy development. Teachers can use this information to differentiate instruction by developmental reading behaviors and characteristics, metacognitive and comprehension strategy needs, instructional reading levels, fluency, and vocabulary understandings.

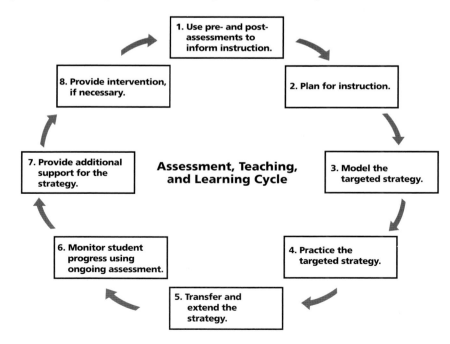

1. Use pre- and post-assessments to inform instruction.

2. Plan for instruction.

3. Model the targeted strategy.

4. Practice the targeted strategy.

5. Transfer and extend the strategy.

6. Monitor student progress using ongoing assessment.

7. Provide additional support for the strategy.

8. Provide intervention, if necessary.

Assessment, Teaching, and Learning Cycle

Rhodes and Shanklin (1993) outline the eleven principles of literacy assessment. Each of these principles is supported in every Benchmark Education Company assessment product.

11 Principles of Literacy Assessment	How BEC Assessment Tools Support the Principles
1. Assess authentic reading and writing.	A variety of ongoing informal assessment tools are available for use before, during, and after literacy instruction.
2. Assess reading and writing in a variety of contexts.	Assessment tools can be administered one-on-one, in small groups, or with the whole class.
3. Assess the literacy environment, instruction, and students.	Assessment tools prompt teacher reflection and provide direction on linking assessment results to instruction.
4. Assess processes as well as products.	Rubrics and assessment tools are available for lesson analysis and noting observable developmental behaviors and characteristics.
5. Analyze error patterns in reading and writing.	Oral reading records and rubrics identify error patterns, strengths, and needs.
6. Consider background knowledge in the assessment of reading and writing.	Student interest questionnaires and surveys gain insight into a students' literacy background and understandings.
7. Base assessment on normal developmental patterns and behavior in reading and writing.	A variety of reading behaviors and characteristics checklists are available to assist in noting developmental milestones and then reporting and planning during assessment meetings.
8. Clarify and use standards in the assessment of reading and writing.	Assessments are aligned with National Literacy Standards and state expectations for learning.
9. Use triangulation to corroborate data and make decisions.	Multiple assessments target different areas of literacy development and are designed to facilitate triangulation of data.
10. Involve students, parents, and other school personnel in the assessment process.	Sharing results from the Benchmark Education Assessments in data team meetings and parent conferences informs and involves others in the process of linking assessment and instruction.
11. Make assessment an ongoing part of everyday reading and writing opportunities and instruction.	Each assessment book provides guidance on how to schedule, manage, organize, and store assessments. Calendars and other planning tools are also provided.

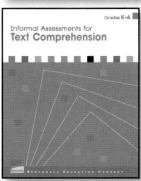

Benchmark Education Company Assessment

The Benchmark Education Company Assessment resources provide tools for ongoing literacy assessments. Each resource has a variety of planning and assessment tools that can be used to inform instruction. Assessment resources can be administered to the whole group, small group, or individual students.

Informal Assessments for Reading Development

- tools for documenting reading behaviors over time, acquisition of concepts about print, and English-language development
- oral reading records
- prompting guides
- reading conference note-taking forms that focus on characteristics of reading development

Informal Assessments for Text Comprehension

- tools for assessing metacognitive and comprehension strategy understandings
- tools for genre and text structure retellings
- comprehension prompting guides
- reading conference note-taking forms that focus on comprehension strategy development

Informal Assessments for Fluency Development

- tools for assessing accuracy, rate, prosody, and oral reading performances
- prompting guides
- reading conference note-taking forms that focus on fluency development

Informal Assessments for Vocabulary Development

- tools for assessing Tier One, Two, and Three vocabulary understandings
- prompting guides
- reading conference note-taking forms that focus on vocabulary development

Informal Assessments for Writing Development

- tools for assessing writing development
- rubric and checklists for assessing genre and text structure
- writing conference note-taking forms

Scheduling, Managing, Organizing, and Storing Assessments

Documenting progress through a cumulative portfolio is one of the greatest advantages of classroom-based assessment. Following are some tips to carry out this process in a teacher- and student-friendly manner.

Scheduling Assessments

Use some assessments as pre- and post-evaluations of growth and development, completing them at the beginning and end of the school year. Conduct other assessments on a more frequent basis as needed. Assess informally during literacy activities every day. Schedule an individual literacy conference with each student every month, and use the information in instructional planning. Hold additional reading and writing conferences as needed to meet students' immediate needs, allowing students to schedule conferences with you as well. Assess students in greatest need of intervention or additional instructional support more frequently—every one to two weeks.

Planning Calendars

Planning calendars help teachers schedule and manage assessments throughout the school year. Teachers can use the masters in the Appendix to note key dates for administering and gathering assessment data for an entire class or individual students.

Year-at-a-Glance Planning Calendar Record state, district, and classroom scheduled assessment dates. (See Appendix page 84)

Month-at-a-Glance Planning Calendar Record progress-monitoring assessments for the entire class or 1–3 students per day. (See Appendix page 85)

Week-at-a-Glance Planning Calendar Record progress-monitoring assessments and individual reading conferences for the week. (See Appendix page 86)

Managing Assessments

Start with one assessment tool and gradually build to the desired collection, as indicated in the following implementation steps.

1. Organize your classroom learning environment. Establish consistent routines and clear expectations for a variety of instructional settings, including whole-group, small-group, and independent activities.

2. Create a management system and schedule for administering formal and informal assessment measures. Identify a simple storage and retrieval system. Set a manageable schedule.

3. Start slowly and proceed one student at a time until all are assessed and you have identified their literacy developmental stages, strengths, and needs.

4. Create class profiles of your findings to serve as a lesson-planning reference and cumulative documentation of growth. Update the profile with each month's individual student conference data.

5. Reflect on the information gathered:

   Are students progressing in a timely fashion?

   What is their overall growth during a specified time frame?

   Are your goals for students being met?

   Is your assessment informing instruction and vice versa?

   Do you see transfer of the skills, strategies, and behaviors you have modeled and taught?

   Do the students in your class reflect the national standards and expectations for their grade level?

Organizing and Storing Assessment Materials

A simple plan for collecting and retrieving each type of record will ensure success and ongoing implementation.

Color code and use separate pocket folders or three-ring binders for each aspect of literacy to be assessed. Have a clearly identified and labeled location to house the individual student assessment folders or binders. Within each folder or binder, use dividers and pockets to store the completed individual assessment tools and work samples.

Store the completed group profile charts in lesson-planning books or create a separate three-ring binder. The binder can serve as an instructional reference tool and cumulative documentation of teaching and learning. Use index tab dividers to note the different profile charts to be collected and used over a school year. Include national, state, and district grade-level recommendations and expectations to complete this instructional reference binder.

Observations and Responsive Teaching

Daily observations of students engaged in meaningful literacy experiences provide detailed information regarding literacy development, strengths, and needs. Documenting observations on a regular basis provides opportunities for teachers to reflect on instruction and areas in need of further assessment. Tomlinson & McTighe remind us that "Responsive teaching suggests a teacher will make modifications in how students get access to important ideas and skills, in ways that students make sense of and demonstrate essential ideas and skills, and in the learning environment—all with an eye to supporting maximum success for each learner." Observations of student learning and transfer provide the link between the assessment and instruction process.

Anecdotal Notes

Anecdotal notes are the observations that are written by the teacher during or after a literacy event. These detailed notes capture students' processing behaviors so they may be further analyzed and used to inform the next instructional move. Anecdotal notes can be taken in whole- or small-group settings or for individuals. These informal notes contain valuable information about students' strengths, weaknesses, progress, needs, processing abilities, or any other observations teachers feel are significant.

Use the Anecdotal Notes master (Appendix page 87) to record notes and observations. Place one small sticky note in each box (one per student). After recording the student's name, date, and your observations, transfer the sticky notes to individual students' portfolios.

What Research Says About Comprehension Assessment

"The purpose of teaching comprehension strategies is to enable children to read with deeper, longer-lasting understanding. We should never lose sight of the goal."

—Keene and Zimmerman, 1997

The ultimate goal of all reading instruction is to provide students with an arsenal of tools they can use to read a wide range of nonfiction (informational, persuasive, procedural, and narrative) and fiction genres with full comprehension. In school, students rely on text comprehension strategies to learn, analyze, and apply nonfiction content-area information. They also require text comprehension strategies to analyze and appreciate literary texts. And we know from research that the skills and strategies that develop good readers are necessary for good writing, too. Benchmark Education Company's resources provide the assessment-driven explicit modeling, guided practice, and independent practice opportunities that guarantees student achieve.

Research About Effective Comprehension Instruction	How *Informal Assessments for Text Comprehension* Supports Best Practices
Development of fluent word-recognition skills can make an important difference in students' understanding of what they read.	Decoding, word study, and fluency instruction are emphasized along with explicit comprehension strategy instruction.
When students are taught vocabulary in a thorough way, their comprehension of what they read improves.	Whole- and small-group resources provide explicit Tier One, Two, and Three vocabulary instruction as well as comprehension strategy instruction.
Reading comprehension can be enhanced by developing a reader's prior knowledge.	The teacher's guide for every big book, leveled text, or mentor text passage includes strategies for building students' prior knowledge and schema around the topic of the text.
Good readers are extremely active as they read. They employ many strategies to think about their thinking and monitor their understanding, memory, and interest level.	Benchmark Education resources provide explicit instruction for all metacognitive "good reader" strategies: Ask questions, visualize, determine text importance, summarize and synthesize, make inferences, and make connections. Lessons also focus on fix-up monitoring strategies.
Effective comprehension strategy instruction should be explicit, or direct (through direct explanation, modeling, guided practice, and help with application of a strategy).	Benchmark Education teacher's guides provide explicit model-guide-apply strategy instruction that scaffolds students toward integration and transfer of strategies to their own reading experiences.
Comprehension strategy instruction can begin in the primary grades. Teachers should emphasize comprehension from the beginning rather than waiting until students have mastered "the basics" of reading.	Explicit instruction begins in Kindergarten with age-appropriate texts and expectations. The developmental scope and sequence of strategies ensures that students build on what they already know from year to year and that over time, they apply strategies to more and more robust literary and content-focused texts.

Observing Metacognitive Strategy Development

Metacognitive strategies are the underlying strategies all good readers apply before, during, and after they read. The reader is actively thinking about a text and monitoring comprehension. We know from the writings of Stephanie Harvey, Anne Goudvis, and Ellin Olliver Keene, among others, that teachers can actively engage students in thinking, talking, and writing about texts. They need to teach students to use specific strategies to think about thinking, and they can learn a lot about students' growth by observing their use of these strategies.

Metacognitive Strategy	Explanation
Ask questions	Readers ask questions before they read. They often pause during reading to ask questions that help them understand and stay involved in what they are reading about. And they sometimes ask questions after they read. Readers ask the following kinds of questions: • Questions about unfamiliar words or confusing information • Questions that have answers written in the text • Questions that have answers that can be inferred from the text • Questions that are not answered in the text and will need further research or discussion
Determine text importance	Readers identify big ideas, themes, and specific information when they read. They may also evaluate the author's purpose and point of view. Readers determine text importance in the following ways: • Activate and build prior knowledge • Determine what is important versus what is interesting • Distinguish between what to read carefully and what to ignore • Highlight important words and nonfiction text features (captions, labels, bullets, etc.) • Make notes and drawings in the margin to understand and remember the text • Determine author's perspective, point of view, and/or opinion
Fix-up monitoring	When comprehension breaks down, readers use fix-up monitoring strategies to repair their comprehension. Some fix-up strategies good readers use are: • Stop and reread to clarify meaning • Read ahead to clarify meaning • Talk about what is confusing in the text • Write about what is confusing in the text

Metacognitive Strategy	Explanation
Make connections	Readers make connections when they link what they are reading to something they already know. Readers make three types of connections to texts: • Text-to-Self: the reader makes a personal connection with the text • Text-to-Text: the reader makes a connection between the text she is reading and a text she has already read • Text-to-World: the reader makes a connection between the text and something in the world at large
Make inferences	Readers make inferences when they use clues and information in a text to figure out something that the author isn't directly telling them. Sometimes readers also use their prior knowledge. Readers make inferences by: • Using story clues to figure out what is happening or why it is happening • Using clues about characters (their actions, words, thoughts) to figure out what they are like and what they might do next • Using clues to figure out the book's themes, or "big ideas"
Summarize and synthesize	Synthesizing is the opposite of analyzing. While analyzing requires readers to take text apart, synthesizing requires readers to put text together to form a new idea or perspective. Readers summarize and synthesize information in the following ways: • Summarize information by stating the big ideas • Make generalizations and judgments, or formulate opinions • Distinguish between more important ideas and less important ideas • Stop to collect their thoughts about a topic before, during, and after reading
Visualize	Readers visualize when they form pictures in their minds to help them "see" and understand characters, settings, objects, and actions they are reading about. Readers visualize by using the following kinds of information: • Vivid verbs that describe actions • Adjectives that describe size, shape, color, and other details • Graphic aids (charts, maps, time lines, diagrams, etc.) that tell size, shape, length, distance, time, and other information • Similes and metaphors that compare one thing to another • Sensory language that evokes how something feels, sounds, smells, or tastes

Ask Questions

Date _____

Directions: Good readers ask questions in order to set their own purposes for reading. During reading, they have inquiries and are always questioning the author's intentions, especially when they have trouble making meaning. After reading, they ask themselves what they've learned and what topics they would like to read more about.

Student	Page	Questions Shared	Before-Reading Questions to Set Purpose for Reading	During-Reading Questions to Clarify Understanding	After-Reading Questions to Extend Comprehension

Informal Assessments for Text Comprehension

Visualize

Date _____

Directions: The act of visualizing assists readers to create pictures in their minds. Visualizing personalizes the reading, keeps the reader engaged, and can prevent the reader from prematurely abandoning a text.

Student	Page	Visualization Shared	Relevant to Information in Book	Expands Information in Book	Ties to Personal Experiences	Shows Evidence of Reflective Thinking	Indicates Interest in Text

Make Connections (Text-to-Self, Text-to-World, Text-to-Text)

Date _____

Directions: Readers naturally make connections between books and their own lives. Readers learn to connect to the content of texts to enhance their own understanding. Prior experiences and background knowledge fuel the connections readers make within texts. Once readers have read a number of books, they begin to connect themes, characters, and issues from one book to another.

Student	Page	Questions Shared	Connected to Prior Experiences	Connected to Background Knowledge About the World	Connected to Other Known Stories or Texts

Informal Assessments for Text Comprehension

Determine Text Importance

Date _____

Directions: Authors often emphasize important ideas and details by mentioning them in headings, placing them first or last within a paragraph, or prefacing them with cue words such as "In fact" or "Most of all." Effective readers use text features and context clues to determine what is important and why the author includes specific information. Ask students to mark important ideas and details with self-stick notes as they read. This encourages them to read critically and helps them better understand and remember key information.

Student	Page	Questions Shared	Important to Topic	Can Explain Why It's Important	Can Identify Text Clues That Emphasize Importance

Make Inferences

Directions: Skilled readers use clues and evidence in a text to figure out things that the author doesn't tell them directly. Ask readers to note clues and evidence with self-stick notes as they read. This encourages them to read actively and to put the clues together to form inferences.

Student	Page	Clues/Evidence	Inference

Summarize and Synthesize

Date _____

Directions: Authors include many facts and details in their texts, but not all of this information is of equal importance. Readers learn to pause occasionally in a text to summarize the most important information. They synthesize this information in order to draw conclusions, make judgments, and formulate opinions. Ask students to share their summaries of the text and to share how they apply their understanding of the text.

Student	Page	Important Information	Summary Statement	Synthesis (Conclusion, Generalization, Judgment, etc)

Monitor-Reading Observation Chart: Discuss Ideas With Others

Small Group: _____   Date: _____

When readers discuss texts or engage in collaborative language acts, they agree or disagree with each other, express confusion when puzzled, seek or give clarification, compare and contrast ideas, offer evidence, express opinions, generalize to new situations, and make connections.

Student's Name	Page	Idea Shared	Supports Thinking with Evidence from Text	Asks Questions of Others to Clarify Thinking	Builds on Others' Ideas at Appropriate Times	Stays on Topic	Comprehends at a Deeper Level

Retell

Date

Directions: During the retelling, readers have the opportunity to reflect on what they are interpreting as they read. Summarizing enables readers to consolidate information and store it in their semantic or long-term memory.

Student	Page	Retell	Uses Own Words	Captures Most Important Information	Demonstrates Understanding of Material	Demonstrates Reflection by Adding Relevant Ideas

Reread

Date _____

Directions: Even the most accomplished reader gets distracted or puzzled from time to time and must reread portions of text. Rereading enables good readers to get back on track, clarify points of confusion, and refine understanding. Ask students to mark passages they have trouble understanding with a self-stick note. Remind them to reread the passage to help them gain an understanding of the author's intended message.

Student	Page	Comment Shared	To Confirm Understanding	To Capture Most Important Information	To Figure Out Tricky Words	To Self-Connect

Informal Assessments for Text Comprehension

Stop, Think, and Write

Date _____

Directions: The act of recording notes requires the reader to decide which sections of the text are worth remembering. Students recall more information when they write about a text. When recording on self-stick notes or in response logs, readers become more conscious of their thinking. They write to describe events, summarize information, formulate beliefs, and explore new ideas.

Student	Page	Notes Recorded	Worth Remembering	Appealed to Beliefs	Raised Questions	Offered New Ideas to Explain

Observing Comprehension Strategy Development

Good readers apply metacognitive strategies to every text they read, but certain texts also require readers to focus on specific text comprehension skills or strategies. In a procedural text, for example, readers pay careful attention to the sequence of events. In a textbook chapter about the causes of the Civil War, students must be able to link causes and their effects. A mystery will feature embedded clues and evidence that good readers look for so that they can make inferences and draw conclusions to solve the mystery. And as they read a persuasive essay or a book review, readers will have to be able to distinguish between the facts and the opinions the author has used to support his or her argument. Every text requires the application of specific comprehension strategies and skills. These are the comprehension strategies and skills students must demonstrate their proficiency with on standardized reading assessments.

The graphic organizers and observational checklists in this section enable teachers to informally assess students' application of specific strategies in the context of small-group and/or independent reading. Each form may be used with any text to evaluate students' level of mastery with the strategies summarized on the chart that follows.

Text Comprehension Strategy	Explanation
Analyze character	Use clues and evidence in the text (character descriptions, dialogue, actions, thoughts) to make inferences about the characters in a text.
Analyze story elements	Examine the literary elements in a story—its characters, setting, and plot—to develop an appreciation and understanding of the work.
Analyze text structure & organization	Use signal words and other clues and evidence to identify how and why the author wrote the text.
Compare & compare	Find ways that two things are alike and different.
Draw conclusions	Determine what the author is suggesting without directly stating it. Conclusions are made during and after reading, and they are made from multiple (3+) pieces of information from the text. Students' conclusions will vary but must be drawn from the evidence in the text and background knowledge.
Evaluate author's purpose	Determine why the author wrote the passage or included specific information or text and graphic features. Authors can have more than one purpose for writing a text. These purposes may include to entertain, to inform, and to persuade. In addition, authors may have many reasons for including specific features in a text, for example, to clarify information, develop characters, and make a reader think.
Distinguish & evaluate fact & opinion	Distinguish between facts and opinions in a text and use this information to make inferences, draw conclusions, and make judgments about the events, characters, and author's purpose.
Identify cause & effect	Find things that happened (effect) and why they happened (cause). Text may contain multiple causes and effects.
Identify stated and unstated main idea & supporting details	Determine what the paragraph, page, or chapter is mostly about. Sometimes the main idea is stated and sometimes it is implied. Students must choose details that support the main idea, not just any detail.
Identify sequence of events	Determine order of events for topics such as history, science, or biography.
Make inferences	Determine what the author is suggesting without directly stating it. Inferences are usually made during reading and are made using one or two pieces of information from the text. Students' inferences will vary but must be made from the evidence in the text and their own background knowledge.
Make judgments	Use facts from the text, and existing beliefs, to evaluate an author's positions or formulate opinions about the characters or situations in a text.
Make predictions	Determine what might happen next in a story or nonfiction piece. Predictions are based on information presented in the text.
Summarize information	Take key ideas from the text and put them together to create a shorter version of the original text. Summaries should have few, if any, details.
Use graphic features to interpret information	Use clues from graphic features (maps, charts, graphs, etc.) to figure out something that is not stated in the text.
Use text features to locate information	Use nonfiction text features (table of contents, index, captions, etc.) to find specific information that is of interest or information that is not stated in the text.

Analyze Character

Name/Page	Clues	Analysis

Analyze Plot

Beginning:

Middle:

End:

Analyze Story Elements

Title:
Author:
Setting:
Characters:
Plot Problems/Events:
Theme/Author's Message:

Name _____ Date _____

Analyze Text Structure and Organization

Page	Text Structure	Clue Words or Phrases

Compare and Contrast

Both

_____   _____

_____   _____

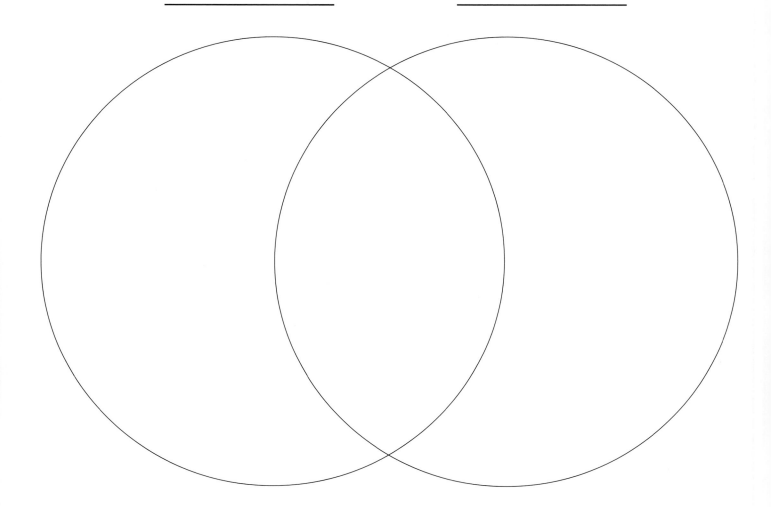

Name _____ Date _____

Compare and Contrast

Page	What Is Being Compared or Contrasted?	How Are They Alike or Different?	Is This a Comparison or a Contrast?
4			
6			
10			
15			
22			
27			
29			

Draw Conclusions

Chapter	Clues/Facts	Conclusion

Evaluate Author's Purpose

Page	Author's Purpose	Evidence

Evaluate Fact and Opinion

Name/Page	Opinion	How do you know that this is an opinion?

Identify Cause and Effect

Page	Cause	Effect

Identify Main Idea and Supporting Details

Page	Main Idea	Supporting Details

Name _____ Date _____

Identify Sequence of Events

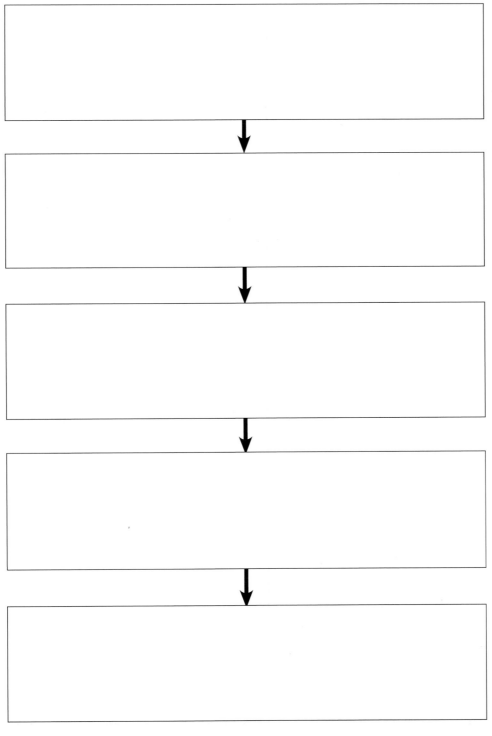

Make Inferences

Page	Clues/Facts	Inference

Make Judgments

Page	Clues/Evidence from the Text	My Prior Knowledge	My Judgments

Make Predictions

Page Number	Question	Prediction	Clues

Name _____ Date _____

Summarize Information

Important Ideas	Summary

Using Graphic Features to Interpret Information

Page	Graphic Feature	Information It Provides

Name _____ Date _____

Use Text Features to Locate Information

Chapter	Text Feature	How the Feature is Used
Chapter		
Chapter		
Chapter		

Comprehension Through Deductive Reasoning Observation Checklist

Directions: Use the following checklist during small-group reading to evaluate students' progress in using higher-level thinking strategies to answer text-dependent questions with deductive reasoning. Record students' names in the first column. Then record specific observations and/or mark **A** for **Always**, **S** for **Sometimes**, and **N** for **Never**.

Behavior	Student's Name	Always	Sometimes	Never	Observations
The student is aware questions ask her to find information in the text.					
The student is aware she must think about what she reads.					
The student understands that words in the question help find the answer in the text passage.					
The student reads and rereads the book to find clues/evidence to answer a question and prove the answer correct.					
The student can explain how she thought about and answered a question.					

Reading Retelling Assessments and Rubrics
(Oral and Written)

Both oral and written individual reading retelling rubrics provide valuable insights about students' reading comprehension and how they go about organizing concepts, ideas, and vocabulary into their own retellings. Seven retelling rubrics—narrative, cause/effect, compare/contrast, sequential/time order, procedural, descriptive, problem/solution—represent the variety of text structures found in Benchmark Education Company texts. Both narrative and expository text are included for use. The instructions for all forms are identical.

After individual assessments are completed, a Group Reading Retelling Chart may be used to create a class or group profile.

Administration

1. Decide which aspect of a student's comprehension you wish to assess and how you want to assess the student (oral or written form). For example, if you want to find out how well a student can identify problems and solutions, choose a chapter book that includes the pattern of problem/solution in the organization of the text. Before meeting with the student, make a copy of the retelling rubric that matches your chosen text structure.

2. Ask the student to read the text silently. If on a previous occasion the student has performed poorly on a retelling while reading silently, you might ask the student to read the text aloud to see if this improves comprehension.

3. Prompt the student to retell in either oral or written form what was read. (Students retell in written form on their own paper.) Allow the student to freely retell what he or she remembers from the text. It may be useful to record some anecdotal notes about the student's performance afterward. Note specific details and vocabulary that the student used.

4. If needed, prompt the student to provide more information. Ask specific questions and allow the student to refer back to the text, if needed. Some helpful questions might include:
   - Can you tell me more about _____?
   - What message do you think the author wanted to convey?
   - What happened after _____?
   - What information did the tables or diagrams give you?
   - What was the problem?
   - What were the solutions that were posed?
   - Do you have any personal experiences that relate to this topic?
   - What effect did the problem have on the event or happening?
   - What ideas or events was the author comparing?
   - Can you tell me more about the characters?

5. Take some anecdotal notes on how the student responded to your questions. Also note whether the student referred to the text to locate an answer.

6. Use the assessment form to rate the student's performance. Place a check mark in the aided or unaided column to note if the student's retelling required prompting. Circle the rubric score.

7. Total and score the rubric as a whole.

8. Record results on a Group Reading Retelling Chart to create a group or class profile.

Using the Results

1. Review the individual rubrics to gain information for future instruction.

2. Identify the areas in which the student is in need of explicit instruction. Observe the same skill on a different text. This in-depth analysis also provides the necessary information for grouping students for specific kinds of instruction.

3. Review the Group Reading Retelling Charts, and identify the text structures needing additional attention at the whole-group, small-group, and independent levels.

Nonfiction Retelling Assessment

Directions: Use the following checklist during small-group reading to evaluate students' skill in retelling information from nonfiction texts. Record students' names in the first column. Then record specific observations and/or mark **+** for **information given with prompts**, ✓ for **information given without prompts**, and **?** for **information not given**.

Student's Name	Explains the Topic	Provides Details to Support the Topic	Provides Details in Appropriate Sequence	Utilizes Appropriate Text Structures, such as Compare/ Contrast or Cause/ Effect	Explains How the Topic Has Personal Relevance

Fiction Retelling Assessment

Directions: Use the following checklist during small-group reading to evaluate students' skill in retelling information from nonfiction texts. Record students' names in the first column. Then record specific observations and/or mark **+** for **information given with prompts**, ✓ for **information given without prompts**, and **?** for **information not given**.

Student's Name	Identifies the Genre	Names the Main Characters in the Story	Identifies the Story's Setting	Describes Plot Details in Sequential Order, including the Beginning, Middle, and End	Explains How the Story has Personal Relevance

Individual Reading Retelling Rubric: Descriptive Text Structure

Name _____   Date _____

Text Title _____   Level _____

Circle one: **Oral Retelling**   **Written Retelling**

Prompt: Tell me about what you read.

Rubric
  4 Gives accurate information using explicit details with elaboration
  3 Gives accurate information with explicit details
  2 Gives limited information, may include some inaccuracies
  1 Unable to give information related to the text
  0 No score indicates no response

	Unaided	Aided	Rubric Score
• Retells story in appropriate sequence			1 2 3 4
• Describes the setting			1 2 3 4
• Provides details about the characters			1 2 3 4
• States the problem and solution of the story			1 2 3 4
• Provides details to support the events in the story			1 2 3 4
• Describes the ending of the story			1 2 3 4
• Explains how the story has personal relevance			1 2 3 4
• Makes connection from the story to other texts			1 2 3 4
Comments:		**Total Rubric Score**	

Individual Reading Retelling Rubric: Narrative Text Structure

Name _____ Date _____

Text Title _____ Level _____

Circle one: **Oral Retelling**   **Written Retelling**

Prompt: Tell me about what you read.

Rubric
- **4** Gives accurate information using explicit details with elaboration
- **3** Gives accurate information with explicit details
- **2** Gives limited information, may include some inaccuracies
- **1** Unable to give information related to the text
- **0** No score indicates no response

	Unaided	Aided	Rubric Score
• States author's intended purpose			1 2 3 4
• Understands and explains key concepts			1 2 3 4
• Provides supportive details for key concepts			1 2 3 4
• Uses descriptive language to help the reader or listener form mind pictures			1 2 3 4
• States setting for information			1 2 3 4
• Provides details in a logical sequence			1 2 3 4
• Demonstrates an understanding of diagrams, tables, or graphs encountered in the text			1 2 3 4
• Provides a summary of the concept and how it has personal relevance			1 2 3 4
Comments:		**Total Rubric Score**	

Individual Reading Retelling Rubric: Problem/Solution Text Structure

Name _____ Date _____

Text Title _____ Level _____

Circle one: **Oral Retelling**   **Written Retelling**

Prompt: Tell me about what you read.

Rubric
- **4** Gives accurate information using explicit details with elaboration
- **3** Gives accurate information with explicit details
- **2** Gives limited information, may include some inaccuracies
- **1** Unable to give information related to the text
- **0** No score indicates no response

	Unaided	**Aided**	**Rubric Score**
• States author's intended purpose			1 2 3 4
• States and understands the importance of the concept			1 2 3 4
• States the problem clearly and why it happens			1 2 3 4
• Provides details about the cause of the problem			1 2 3 4
• Provides details that state the effects of the problem			1 2 3 4
• Clearly links causes and effects			1 2 3 4
• Provides a realistic solution to the problem			1 2 3 4
• Demonstrates an understanding of diagrams, tables, or graphs encountered in the text			1 2 3 4
• Provides a summary of the concept and how it has personal relevance			1 2 3 4
		Total Rubric Score	

Comments:

Individual Reading Retelling Rubric: Sequential/Time Order Text Structure

Name _____ Date _____

Text Title _____ Level _____

Circle one: **Oral Retelling**   **Written Retelling**

Prompt: Tell me about what you read.

Rubric

4 Gives accurate information using explicit details with elaboration
3 Gives accurate information with explicit details
2 Gives limited information, may include some inaccuracies
1 Unable to give information related to the text
0 No score indicates no response

	Unaided	Aided	Rubric Score
• States author's intended purpose			1 2 3 4
• Retells events in chronological order or logical sequence			1 2 3 4
• Provides details to support the key concepts			1 2 3 4
• Demonstrates an understanding of diagrams, tables, or graphs encountered in the text			1 2 3 4
• Provides a summary of the concept and how it has personal relevance			1 2 3 4
Comments:		**Total Rubric Score**	

Individual Reading Retelling Rubric:
Procedural Text Structure

Name _____   Date _____

Text Title _____   Level _____

Circle one: **Oral Retelling**   **Written Retelling**

Prompt: Tell me about what you read.

Rubric
4 Gives accurate information using explicit details with elaboration
3 Gives accurate information with explicit details
2 Gives limited information, may include some inaccuracies
1 Unable to give information related to the text
0 No score indicates no response

	Unaided	Aided	Rubric Score
• States author's intended purpose			1 2 3 4
• Includes material, equipment, or ingredients needed			1 2 3 4
• Retells a detailed step-by-step sequence of how and when to do something in order to accomplish a task			1 2 3 4
• Demonstrates an understanding of diagrams, tables, or graphs encountered in the text			1 2 3 4
• Provides a summary of the concept or task and how it has personal relevance			1 2 3 4
		Total Rubric Score	

Comments:

Individual Reading Retelling Rubric:
Compare/Contrast Text Structure

Name _____ Date _____

Text Title _____ Level _____

Circle one: **Oral Retelling**   **Written Retelling**

Prompt: Tell me about what you read.

Rubric

  4 Gives accurate information using explicit details with elaboration
  3 Gives accurate information with explicit details
  2 Gives limited information, may include some inaccuracies
  1 Unable to give information related to the text
  0 No score indicates no response

	Unaided	Aided	Rubric Score
• States author's intended purpose			1 2 3 4
• Understands and explains the key concepts			1 2 3 4
• Clearly compares the topic by providing at least two similarities and at least two differences			1 2 3 4
• Demonstrates an understanding of diagrams, tables, or graphs encountered in the text			1 2 3 4
• Provides a summary of the concept and how it has personal relevance			1 2 3 4
		Total Rubric Score	

Comments:

Individual Reading Retelling Rubric:
Cause/Effect Text Structure

Name _____   Date _____

Text Title _____   Level _____

Circle one: **Oral Retelling**   **Written Retelling**

Prompt: Tell me about what you read.

Rubric
- **4** Gives accurate information using explicit details with elaboration
- **3** Gives accurate information with explicit details
- **2** Gives limited information, may include some inaccuracies
- **1** Unable to give information related to the text
- **0** No score indicates no response

	Unaided	Aided	Rubric Score
• States author's intended purpose			1 2 3 4
• States and understands the importance of the concept			1 2 3 4
• States the event or happening			1 2 3 4
• Provides details about the cause of the event			1 2 3 4
• Provides details about the effect of the happening or event			1 2 3 4
• Clearly links causes and effects			1 2 3 4
• Demonstrates an understanding of diagrams, tables, or graphs encountered in the text			1 2 3 4
• Provides a summary of the concept and how it has personal relevance			1 2 3 4
Comments:		**Total Rubric Score**	

Individual Writing Assessment:
Descriptive Frames

Name _____ Date _____

Title _____

• **What is the main idea?**

• **What are the attributes of the main idea?**

• **What is the function of each attribute?**

Individual Writing Assessment: Problem/Solution Frames

Name _____ Date _____

Title _____

- **What is the problem?**

- **Who or what has the problem?**

- **What is causing the problem?**

- **What are the immediate effects of the problem?**

- **What are the long-lasting effects of the problem?**

- **Who is trying to solve the problem?**

- **What solutions are being tried?**

- **What are the obstacles to the solutions?**

- **What are the result of the attempts of the solutions?**

- **How is the problem resolved?**

Individual Writing Assessment:
Sequential/Time Order Frames

Name _____ Date _____

Title _____

- **What is the beginning event?**

- **What happened next?**

- **What happened after that?**

- **How are the events related?**

- **What is the final outcome?**

Individual Writing Assessment: Procedural Frames

Name _____ Date _____

Title _____

• **What is the procedure or event?**

• **What are the steps?**

• **How do the steps relate to one another?**

• **What is the end result?**

Individual Writing Assessment: Compare/Contrast Frames

Name _____ Date _____

Title _____

- **Describe what is being compared and contrasted.**

- **What attributes are being used to compare and contrast?**

- **What makes the objects similar?**

- **What makes the objects different?**

Individual Writing Assessment: Cause/Effect Frames

Name _____ Date _____

Title _____

• **What happens?**

• **What causes the event to happen?**

• **What are the effects of the event?**

Individual Writing Assignment: Narrative Frames

Name _____ Date _____

Title _____

BEGINNING

SETTING: **Where** does the story take place?
When does the story take place?
Who is the main character?

PROBLEM: **What** is the problem?

MIDDLE   **What** are the events in the story that make an attempt to solve the problem?

END

RESOLUTION: **How** is the problem solved?

REACTIONS: **How** do the characters feel about the resolution?

THEME: **What** is the overall moral or theme of the story?

Reading Conferences

Individual Reading Conferences provide teachers with an opportunity to reflect on the metacogntive and comprehension strategies students have practiced during whole- and small-group instruction or applied during independent reading. Teachers can encourage the use of academic vocabulary for comprehension, they can validate strategies students have used well, and discuss strategies students might apply to help them in the future. Some conferences may involve reviewing and discussing a comprehension graphic organizer students have completed during independent workstation time. The Reading Conference recording form provides a template for key elements to include in your reading conferences. Based on the conference, you may choose to provide additional support through mini-lessons, prompts (see also pages 66–78), or discussions related to comprehension strategy development.

Individual Reading Conference

Name: _____ Date: _____

Book Title: _____ Author: _____ Pages: ____ to ____

Part One: Independent Reading Recap

Why did you choose this book? What are you interested in reading about? Do you need help finding a new book?

How is the difficulty of the text for you? How do you know?

Summarize or retell what has been happening (or what you have learned) so far.

Tell me what you remember most about what you've read.

Notes: _____

_____

_____

_____

_____

_____

_____

Part Two: Comprehension Strategy Connections

How have you used the metacognitive and comprehension strategies we've been learning about as a reader?

How have they helped you understand what you are reading? Explain.

How do you know when you have a break down in understanding what you are reading? How do you adjust your reading and solve your problems? How does that help you understand, or comprehend, the text more?

Notes: _____

_____

_____

_____

_____

_____

_____

Part Three: Oral Reading Record

Conduct an oral reading record on the independent reading selection or from a text read previously in small-group guided reading lessons.

Attach the oral reading record form to your Individual Reading Conference note-taking form when finished.

Record notes for observations and next steps instructionally below.

Notes: _____

_____

_____

_____

_____

_____

_____

_____

Part Four: Action Planning

What are your strengths/needs/goals as a reader? How can I help you achieve them?

When do you anticipate finishing this book?

What is next on your list of must-read titles?

Notes: _____

_____

_____

_____

_____

_____

_____

Prompting to Support Comprehension Strategy Development

As an observant and responsive teacher, having a variety of prompting stems for a variety of purposes is a valuable resource. Each type of prompt has a distinct purpose for supporting learning and increasing proficiency with the elements of comprehension.

Prompting Type	Purpose
Goal Oriented	Prompts for the reader who is not using the targeted strategy or skill at all. They offer a model or a benchmark of how the strategy or skill is used in reading.
Corrective Feedback/ Directive	Prompts for students who are beginning to use the strategy or skill but still need direct teaching or coaching on how to use it properly.
Self-Monitoring/ Reflective	Prompts for students who have previously exhibited use of the strategy or skill in reading but are not consistent. These prompts remind students to be more reflective and think about the importance of using the strategy or skill at the right time.
Validating/Confirming	Prompts that are used at any time to validate or confirm a student's reading strategies and skills.

The following pages contain prompting stems to support the use of a wide range of comprehension strategies. Use the prompts during guided practice or during independent reading. Remember to continually ask students to reflect on how they used strategies to support their comprehension. This will promote awareness of the link between active reading and comprehension and aid in encouraging students to reflect and monitor reading to maintain understanding at all times.

Analyze Character Prompts

Goal Oriented
- I am going to read slowly and reread if necessary to find clues.
- I am going to use clues in the text and what I know to identify character traits.
- The clue word(s) _____ show that the character is _____.

Directive and Corrective Feedback
- What other sentences contain clues to the person's character?
- Which details are clues to the person's character? How can you tell?
- What do the clues tell you about the character?

Self-Monitoring and Reflection
- What could you do to figure out a character's motivation?
- What visualizations would help you understand the character better?
- How does reading about what a character does show what the character is like?

Validating and Confirming
- Great job identifying the character's traits and motivation!
- You found all the evidence that shows the character's traits and motivation.
- I like the way you visualized to clarify your understanding of the character.

Analyze Story Elements Prompts

Goal Oriented
- I am going to read slowly to identify and understand the characters, setting, and plot.
- I am going to summarize and synthesize as I read to help me analyze story elements.
- The plot is made up of these events: _____.

Directive and Corrective Feedback
- How can you tell how the characters feel?
- What is the setting? Why is it important?
- How can you tell what the problem is?
- What clues tell you what the solution is?

Self-Monitoring and Reflection
- What could you do to help yourself understand the plot and characters better?
- What details tell where and when the story takes place?
- How did you summarize the story? How did you use your own experiences to synthesize?

Validating and Confirming
- You really understand the story elements in this passage.
- You did a great job of identifying the problem and the solution in the plot.
- I like the way you summarized the plot events and synthesized them with your own experiences.

Compare & Contrast Prompts

Goal Oriented
- I am going to read slowly so I will notice the signal language.
- The signal word _____ lets me know the author is comparing things.
- The signal word _____ lets me know the author is contrasting things.

Directive and Corrective Feedback
- Read the sentence. What word signals a comparison?
- How are the things alike?
- Read the sentence. What word signals a contrast?
- How are the things different?

Self-Monitoring and Reflection
- What could you do to help yourself recognize a comparison or contrast?
- Did you try to identify the most important information? What words and phrases helped you do this?

Validating and Confirming
- You really understand what the author was comparing and contrasting.
- You really picked up on the signal language. Great job!
- I like how you identified comparisons and contrasts even when there was no signal language to help you.
- I like the way you determined important information to clarify your understanding.

Draw Conclusions Prompts

Goal Oriented

- I am going to read slowly to find evidence that proves an idea the author did not state.
- I am going to think about what conclusion would be reasonable on the basis of the evidence.
- Using the evidence and what I know, I can draw the conclusion that _____ .

Directive and Corrective Feedback

- What does that particular clue suggest?
- Does all of the evidence lead to that conclusion? Or could other conclusions be drawn?
- Is that a reasonable conclusion? Does it make sense when you review the evidence?

Self-Monitoring and Reflection

- What unstated ideas are implied by these facts?
- What does that clue allow you to infer, or guess, about the text?
- How did your previous experiences help you interpret clues and draw conclusions?

Validating and Confirming

- Great job figuring out what the author is suggesting with these clues!
- You did an excellent job finding all the clues and using what you know to draw a valid conclusion.
- I like the way you made inferences to clarify your understanding of the text.

Evaluate Author's Purpose Prompts

Goal Oriented
- I am going to look for clues that show the author's purpose.
- I am going to summarize and synthesize to find the author's purpose.
- The clue in sentence _____ shows that the purpose is _____.

Directive and Corrective Feedback
- Does that sentence help you figure out the author's purpose?
- Which details show the author's purpose? How can you tell?
- What do the clues tell you about the author's purpose?

Self-Monitoring and Reflection
- What could you do to figure out the author's purpose?
- How could you summarize and synthesize to find the author's purpose?
- How does identifying how the text makes you feel help you identify the author's purpose?

Validating and Confirming
- Great job identifying the author's purpose!
- You found all the clues that show the author's purpose.
- I like the way you summarized and synthesized to help identify the author's purpose.

Distinguish & Evaluate Fact & Opinion Prompts

Goal Oriented
- I am going to ask whether a statement can be proved or not to distinguish between a fact and an opinion.
- I am going to look for signal words to opinions such as **think**, **believe**, **best**, and **worst**.
- This sentence is a(n) _____ because _____.

Directive and Corrective Feedback
- Can that sentence be proven true or false?
- Does the sentence contain a signal word such as **believe** or **best**?
- What connections can you make to help you identify the fact or opinion?

Self-Monitoring and Reflection
- What could you do to figure out whether a statement is a fact or an opinion?
- What connections could you make to your life, the world, or other texts?
- How does identifying clues and signal words help you identify facts and opinions?

Validating and Confirming
- Great job identifying facts and opinions!
- You found signal words that helped you identify opinions.
- I like the way you made connections to help you recognize facts and opinions.

Identify Cause & Effect Prompts

Goal Oriented
- I am going to read slowly to look for causes and effects.
- I am going to read slowly to identify the signal language for cause and effect.
- The word(s) _____ let(s) me know the author is telling about a cause-and-effect relationship.

Directive and Corrective Feedback
- Does that word (phrase) signal a cause-and-effect relationship?
- What is the cause? What clue(s) told you this is a cause?
- What is the effect? What clue(s) told you this is an effect?

Self-Monitoring and Reflection
- What could you do to help yourself understand the cause-and-effect relationships better?
- What connections can you make to the text?
- How does identifying the signal language for cause and effect help you identify causes and effects?

Validating and Confirming
- You really understand the causes and effects in this text.
- You did a great job of noticing the signal language for cause and effect.
- I like the way you made connections to clarify your understanding of the text.

Identify Main Idea & Supporting Details Prompts

Goal Oriented
- I am going to read slowly to find the main idea.
- I am going to read slowly to find details that tell more about the main idea.
- The details in sentence _____ support the main idea _____.

Directive and Corrective Feedback
- Does that sentence tell the most important idea of the passage?
- Which details are important? How can you tell?
- What do the details tell you about the main idea?

Self-Monitoring and Reflection
- What could you do to figure out the main idea?
- What questions could you ask yourself?
- How does identifying key words help you identify important details?

Validating and Confirming
- Great job identifying the main idea!
- You found all the details that tell more about the main idea.
- I like the way you asked yourself questions and identified important words to clarify your understanding.

Identify Sequence of Events Prompts

Goal Oriented
- I am going to read slowly to notice any signal language for sequence of events.
- I am going to use the signal language to help me identify the sequence of events.
- The words _____ let me know when these events happened.

Directive and Corrective Feedback
- Does that word (phrase) tell about time order?
- Read the sentence. What words help you know when something happened? What event happened?
- What event happened first? How do you know?
- What happened next? What clues help you know?

Self-Monitoring and Reflection
- What could you do to help yourself understand sequence of events better?
- What questions could you ask yourself?
- Did you try to identify the most important information? What words and phrases helped you do this?

Validating and Confirming
- You really understand what steps the author was describing.
- You really picked up on the signal language for sequence of events. Good job!
- I like the way you identified the sequence of events even when there were no signal words to help you.
- I like the way you determined the most important text to clarify your understanding.

Make Inferences Prompts

Goal Oriented

- I am going to read slowly and reread if necessary to locate clues.
- I am going to think about clues in the text and what I know to make inferences.
- The clue word(s) _____ help me figure out, or infer, that _____.

Directive and Corrective Feedback

- Does that phrase (sentence) provide a clue to what the author does not state directly?
- Read the sentence. What information could help you understand what the author means?
- What inference can you make? What helped you make the inference?

Self-Monitoring and Reflection

- What could you do to help yourself make an inference?
- What visualizations could you make?
- Did you use clues to help you make an inference? Did you reread if you did not understand the text?

Validating and Confirming

- You did a good job picking up on what the author did not state directly.
- You really picked up on the evidence to make an inference. Great job!
- I like the way you visualized to help you make inferences.
- I like the way you monitored your understanding and reread when necessary.

Make Judgments Prompts

Goal Oriented
- To figure out the judgment the author makes, I will think about why the author wrote the passage and what key idea the evidence supports.
- The following evidence _____ supports the judgment that _____.

Directive and Corrective Feedback
- Which details are most important? Why do you need to know that?
- What do the details tell you about the author's judgment?
- If the author's judgment is not stated in the passage, how can you use your own words to state the author's judgment?

Self-Monitoring and Reflection
- What could you do to help yourself figure out the judgment the author is making?
- What questions could you ask yourself?
- How does identifying reasons or important details help you recognize the author's judgment?

Validating and Confirming
- You did a great job of figuring out what judgment the author makes in the passage.
- You really picked up on the evidence that supports the author's judgment.
- I like the way you asked yourself questions to clarify your understanding of the author's argument.

Make Predictions Prompts

Goal Oriented

- I am going to read slowly and reread to find and think about clues to what will happen.
- I am going to use clues in the text and what I know to make predictions.
- The clue phrase(s) _____ help(s) me predict that _____.

Directive and Corrective Feedback

- Does this part of the text give you ideas about what might happen?
- How does this sentence help you predict what might happen? What do you already know that helps you predict what might happen?
- What other predictions can you make? What clues in the text helped you make these predictions?

Self-Monitoring and Reflection

- What inferences could you make about this text? How could they help you make a prediction?
- How might visualizing what this part tells help you make a prediction?
- What do you already know that can help you predict what will happen?

Validating and Confirming

- Great job making predictions!
- You identified all the clues to help you make predictions.
- I like the way you used what you already know to help you predict what would happen.
- You did a good job of visualizing, or picturing what was happening, to understand the text.

Summarize Information Prompts

Goal Oriented

- I am going to read carefully and watch for key words and phrases.
- I am going to think about which ideas are most important as I read.
- _____ is an important idea in this passage, and I will include it in my summary.

Directive and Corrective Feedback

- How could you restate this part in your own words to show what it means?
- How does that part relate to the main point of the text?
- Why didn't you include the idea _____?

Self-Monitoring and Reflection

- What could you do to help yourself sum up the most important ideas in fewer words?
- How could retelling the text in your own words help you?
- Did you identify key words and phrases? How did they help you identify important ideas?

Validating and Confirming

- Great job identifying the big ideas!
- You really understood how to sum up the most important information in a few words.
- I like the way you monitored your understanding and used the fix-up strategy _____ to help you.

Comprehension and Text Understanding

When assessing comprehension and text understanding, Fountas and Pinnell remind us that "when you are looking at readers in your classroom, you have what the reader says and does to inform your teaching and evaluation. You form hypotheses about the reader's thinking from these two categories: (1) the act, or the process, of reading (what the reader does); and (2) the reader's response to reading through talk, writing, or other venues (what the reader says)." Reference the developmental characteristics of readers over time found in *Informal Assessments for Reading Development* on analyze reading behaviors and characteristics at various stages of development. In addition, as you reflect on key developmental characteristics and how readers interact with instructional-level texts, also take into account their level of text comprehension and metacognitive understandings. To assess comprehension, ask questions (open-ended, multiple choice, constructed-response items), use rubrics, and written, oral, or artistic responses to evaluate understandings from various levels of comprehension. As you evaluate student responses, identify needs for metacognitive and comprehension strategy instruction.

Comprehension can be examined from literal, interpretive, and applied levels of understanding. Bloom's Taxonomy identifies the six levels within the cognitive domain in a hierarchy from the lowest level (simple recall) to the highest level (evaluation). When evaluating student responses and answers to comprehension questions, consider where their strengths and needs are from literal to inferential levels of thinking and understanding.

Levels of Bloom's Taxonomy	Description & Verbs for Comprehension Questions and Discussions
Knowledge	Remembering or recalling how many, when, where list, tell, describe, identify, arrange, define, name, order, relate, recall, repeat
Understanding/Comprehension	Grasping or understanding the meaning of text describe, discuss, explain, express, identify, locate, restate, review, select
Application	Apply previously learned information to new and unfamiliar situations apply, choose, demonstrate, dramatize, illustrate, interpret, sketch, show, use, write
Analysis	Breaking information into parts analyze, categorize, compare, contrast, criticize, differentiate, distinguish, question
Synthesis	Apply prior knowledge and combine into new understandings arrange, combine, compose, construct, create, design, organize, propose
Evaluation	Judging and deciding against a set criteria argue, assess, conclude, compare, defend, judge, explain, predict, rate, select, support, summarize, evaluate

Perkins identifies the following four levels of metacognition. As teachers assess students and engage in individual reading conferences and discussions, identify the level of metacognitive awareness that reflects each student's understanding of strategies and how they use the strategies flexibly for problem solving and active, strategic reading.

Level of Metacognitive Knowledge	Description
Tacit Level	Being unaware of our metacognitive knowledge
Awareness Level	Knowing about some kinds of thinking we do (generating ideas, finding evidence), but not being strategic
Strategic Level	Organizing our thinking by using problem solving, decision making, evidence seeking, and other techniques
Reflective Level	Being strategic and reflecting on our thinking in progress, pondering strategies, and revising them accordingly

How do teachers make an authentic connection between strategy instruction and isolated test taking situations in which students are asked to apply specific strategies? During standardized reading assessments, students are required to answer different levels of text-dependent comprehension questions. These questions require application of different levels of Bloom's Taxonomy and metacognitive knowledge. Keep these question levels in mind to focus on comprehension development. During small-group reading, use prompts (see the charts on page 81–82) about the texts being read to provide opportunities for students to rehearse strategies for answering each type of question. Use the assessment checklist on page 84 to evaluate students' use of text-dependent comprehension strategies and provide reteaching opportunities as needed.

Text-Dependent Comprehension Questions

Comprehension Question Type	Explanation	Comprehension Strategies Students May Need to Apply	Sample Question Stems
Level 1 Find It!	These questions have answers right in the text. Reread to locate facts and details to answer the questions.	Identify facts and details Identify characters Identify setting	This story takes place in… What is the _____? When did _____ happen?
Level 2 Look Closer!	The answers are in the text, but you may need to look in more than one place to find them.	Identify sequence of events Identify cause and effect Compare and contrast Identify stated main ideas	**Identify sequence of events** After (year), what happened? When can you _____? **Identify cause and effect** Why did _____ need to _____? What causes _____ to happen? **Compare and contrast** How are _____ and _____ alike? How are they different? What do _____ and _____ have in common? **Identify stated main ideas and supporting details** What details support the main idea that _____? What sentence best states the main idea?

Text-Dependent Comprehension Questions (continued)

Comprehension Question Type	Explanation	Comprehension Strategies Students May Need to Apply	Sample Question Stems
Level 3 Prove It!	You'll have to be a detective. You won't find the exact answers to these questions, but you will find clues and evidence to support your inferences and conclusions.	Make inferences Draw conclusions Make predictions Analyze character Summarize information Identify unstated main ideas Use graphic features to interpret information	**Make inferences** What can you infer from paragraph _____? Which sentence from the story/passage shows you _____? **Draw conclusions** From the information in this passage, you can conclude that… In what way is _____ important in the text? **Make predictions** What will [character] probably do in the future? What clues/evience would support the prediction that…? **Analyze character** What clues tell you that [character] is …? You can tell that [character] is… **Summarize information** Which sentence best completes the summary? Which is the best summary? **Identify unstated main ideas** This passage is mostly about _____. **Use graphic features to interpret information** What can you tell from the diagram in this passage? What does the bar graph tell you?
Level 4 Take It Apart!	These questions require students to think about the text structure and organization and the author's purpose for including specific text and graphic features.	Evaluate author's purpose Analyze text structure and organization	**Evaluate author's purpose** The author probably included paragraph _____ so that _____. The most likely reason the author wrote this passage was to _____. The author probably included the chart so that _____. **Analyze text structure and organization** The author uses a ___ structure to organize ___. Give an example. What text structure did the author use to organize paragraphs _____ and _____? How does the author organize this passage?

Assessment Checklist

Name _____ Date _____

Text _____ Level _____

Use the following checklist to evaluate students' use of strategies to answer text-dependent comprehension questions.

Behavior	Always	Sometimes	Never
1. The student can identify the level of question he is being asked.			
2. The student can identify what the question requires her to do (for example, locate facts, identify cause and effect, compare and contrast, etc.).			
3. The student can identify words in the question that will help him find the answer in the text passage.			
4. The student can find information in the text passage that answers the question or supports the answer.			
5. The student can explain the process she used to answer the question.			

Based on your assessment of students' performance, use the following tips to revisit and reteach.

1. If the student cannot identify the correct question level . . .
Review the four types of comprehension questions and what the questions look like at each level.

2. If the student cannot identify what the question is asking her to do . . .
Review the comprehension strategies commonly targeted in questions at each level.
Refer to the list of comprehension strategies provided for each question level.

3. If the student cannot identify words in the question that will help him find the answer in the text passage . . .
Review how to recognize key words in the question for each comprehension strategy.
Use the sample questions provided on the Comprehension Through Deductive Reasoning Power Tool Flip Chart.

4. If the student understands what the question is asking but cannot find the answer in the text . . .
Model how to skim the text to look for answers or clues and key phrases. (Use the examples in the "Clues to Look For" boxes for each question level on the Comprehension Through Deductive Reasoning Power Tool Flip Chart.)

5. If the student can answer the question successfully but cannot explain how she came up with the answer . . .
Model the steps used to answer the question by creating a steps-in-a-process graphic organizer. Ask the student to retell her process using the graphic organizer.

Comments

Year-at-aGlance Planning Calendar

Teacher Name: _____ Grade: _____ Level: _____

Notes:	August	September	October
November	**December**	**January**	**February**
March	**April**	**May**	**June**

Informal Assessments for Text Comprehension   ©2011 Benchmark Education Company, LLC

Month-at-a-Glance Planning Calendar

Teacher Name: _____ Grade: _____ Level: _____

	Monday	Tuesday	Wednesday	Thursday	Friday
Week of:					
Week of:					
Week of:					
Week of:					

Week-at-a-Glance Planning Calendar

Teacher Name: _____   Grade: _____   Level: _____

	Monday	Tuesday	Wednesday	Thursday	Friday
Progress-Monitoring Assessments					
Individual Reading Conferences					

Anecdotal Notes

Teacher Name: _____

Grade: _____   Level: _____

Adams, M. J., B. Foorman, I. Lundberg, and T. Beeler. *Phonemic Awareness in Young Children*. Baltimore, MD: Brookes Publishing Company, 1998.

Afflerback, P. *Understanding and Using Reading Assessment, K-12*. IRA, 2007.

Anderson, C. *How's It Going? A Practical Guide to Conferring With Students*. Portsmouth, NH: Heinemann, 2000.

Barrentine, S., ed. *Reading Assessment: Principles and Practices for Elementary Teachers*. IRA, 1999.

Bear, D. B., M. Invernizzi, S. Templeton, and F. Johnson. *Words Their Way: A Developmental Approach to Phonics, Spelling, and Vocabulary K–8*. New York: Macmillan/Merrill, 1996.

Beaver, J. *Developmental Reading Assessment*. Parsippany, NJ: Celebration Press, 1997.

Beaver, T. *The Author's Profile: Assessing Writing in Context*. Portland, ME: Stenhouse, 1998.

Boyd-Barstone, P. "Focused Anecdotal Records Assessment: A Tool for Standards-based, Authentic Assessment." *The Reading Teacher* 58 (3) (2004): 230–239.

Clay, M. *An Observation Survey of Early Literacy Achievement*. Portsmouth, NH: Heinemann, 1993.

Cobb, C. "Effective Instruction Begins with Purposeful Assessments" in *Reading Assessment: Principles and Practices for Elementary Teachers* (2nd edition). IRA, 2005.

Cunningham, P. *Phonics They Use: Words for Reading and Writing*, 3rd edition. Upper Saddle River, NJ: Addison-Wesley Longman, 2000.

Dorn, L., C. French, and T. Jones. *Apprenticeship in Literacy: Transitions Across Reading and Writing*. Portland, ME: Stenhouse, 1998.

Doughtery Stahl, K. A., and M. A. Bravo. "Contemporary Classroom Vocabulary Assessment for Content Areas." *The Reading Teacher* 63 (7) (2010): 566–578.

Duke, N., and P. D. Pearson. "Effective Practices for Developing Reading Comprehension" in A. E. Farstrup and S. Samuels, eds. *What Research Has to Say About Reading Instruction* (pp. 204–242). IRA, 2002.

Fiderer, A. *Practical Assessments for Literature-Based Reading Classrooms*. New York: Scholastic, 1995.

Fiene, J. M., and S. McMahon. "Assessing Comprehension: A Classroom-Based Process." *The Reading Teacher* 60 (5) (2007): 406–417.

Fletcher, R., and J. Portalupi. *Craft Lessons: Teaching Writing K–8*. Portland, ME: Stenhouse, 1998.

Fletcher, R., and J. Portalupi. *Nonfiction Craft Lessons: Teaching Information Writing K–8.* Portland, ME: Stenhouse, 2001.

Fountas, I., and G. Pinnell. *Guided Reading: Good First Teaching for All Children.* Portsmouth, NH: Heinemann, 1996.

Fountas, I., and G. Pinnell. *Matching Texts to Readers.* Portsmouth, NH: Heinemann, 1999.

Fountas, I., and G. Pinnell, eds. *Voices on Word Matters: Learning About Phonics and Spelling in the Literacy Classroom.* Portsmouth, NH: Heinemann, 1999.

Fry, E., J. Kress, and D. L. Fountoukidis. *The Reading Teacher's Book of Lists*, 3rd edition. Upper Saddle River, NJ: Prentice Hall, 1993.

Gentry, J. R. *The Literacy Map: Guiding Children to Where They Need to Be K–3.* New York: Mondo, 2000.

Gentry, J. R. *My Kid Can't Spell: Understanding and Assisting Your Child's Literacy Development.* Portsmouth, NH: Heinemann, 1997.

Gentry, J. R., and J. Gillet. *Teaching Kids to Spell.* Portsmouth, NH: Heinemann, 1993.

Gill, S. R. "The Comprehension Matrix: A Tool for Designing Comprehension Instruction." *The Reading Teacher* 62 (2) (2008): 106–113.

Glazer, S. M. *Assessment Is Instruction: Reading, Writing, Spelling, and Phonics for All Learners.* Norwood, MA: Christopher-Gordon, 1998.

Harvey, S. *Nonfiction Matters: Reading, Writing, and Research in Grades 3–8.* Portland, ME: Stenhouse, 1998.

Harvey, S., and A. Goudvis. *Strategies That Work: Teaching Comprehension to Enhance Understanding.* Portland, ME: Stenhouse, 2000.

Helman, L. A. "Using Literacy Assessment Results to Improve Teaching for English-Language Learners." *The Reading Teacher* 58 (7) (2005): 668–677.

Hill, B., C. Ruptic, and L. Norwick. *Classroom Based Assessment.* Norwood, MA: Christopher-Gordon, 1998.

Hindley, J. *In the Company of Children.* Portland, ME: Stenhouse, 1996.

International Reading Association and National Council of Teachers of English. *Standards for the Assessment of Reading and Writing* (revised). IRA, 2010.

Israel, S. E. *Using Metacognitive Assessments to Create Individualized Reading Instruction.* IRA, 2007.

Johnston, P. *Assessment Conversations. Reading Assessment: Principles and Practices for Elementary Teachers* (2nd edition). IRA, 2005.

Johnston, P. *Knowing Literacy: Constructive Literacy Assessment.* Portland, ME: Stenhouse, 1997.

Johnston, P., and P. Costell. Principles for Literacy Assessment. *Reading Research Quarterly* 40 (2) (2005): 256–267.

Keene, E., and S. Zimmerman. *Mosaic of Thought*. Portsmouth, NH: Heinemann, 1997.

Lenski, S. D., F. Ehlers-Zavala, M. C. Daniel, and X. Sun-Irminger. "Assessing English-Language Learners in Mainstream Classrooms." *The Reading Teacher* 60 (1) (2006): 24–34.

McKenna, M. C., and S. Walpole. "How Well Does Assessment Inform Our Reading Instruction?" *The Reading Teacher* 59 (1) (2005): 84–86.

National Center on Education and the Economy. *Reading and Writing Grade by Grade: Primary Literacy Standards*. Rockville, MD: Smith Lithograph Corporation, 1999.

Opitz, M., and M. Ford. "Assessment Can Be Friendly!" *The Reading Teacher* 59 (8) (2006): 814–816.

Paris, A. H., and S. G. Paris. "Assessing Narrative Comprehension in Young Children." *Reading Research Quarterly* 38 (1) (2003): 36–76.

Pearson, P. D., E. H. Hiebert, and M. L. Kamil. "Vocabulary Assessment: What We Know and What We Need to Know." *Reading Research Quarterly* 42 (2) (April/May/June 2007): 282–296.

Perkins, D. *Smart Schools: Better Thinking and Learning for Every Child*. New York: Simon & Schuster, 1995.

Pinnell, G., and I. Fountas. *Word Matters: Teaching Phonics and Spelling in the Reading-Writing Classroom*. Portsmouth, NH: Heinemann, 1998.

Power, B. *Taking Note: Improving Your Observational Notetaking*. Portland, ME: Stenhouse, 1996.

Rhodes, L., and N. Shanklin. *Windows Into Literacy: Assessing Learners K–8*. Portsmouth, NH: Heinemann, 1993.

Risko, V. J., and D. Walker-Dolhouse. "Making the Most of Assessments to Inform Instruction." *The Reading Teacher* (February 2010): 420–422.

Robb, L. *Easy to Manage Reading and Writing Conferences*. New York: Scholastic, 1998.

Routman, R. *Conversations*. Portsmouth, NH: Heinemann, 2000.

Serafini, F. *Classroom Reading Assessment: More Efficient Ways to View and Evaluate Your Readers*. Portsmouth, NH: Heinemann, 2010.

Tomlinson, C. A., and J. McTighe. Integrating Differentiated Instruction and Understanding Design. ASCD, 2006.

Weaver, C. *Reading Process: Reading Process and Practice* (Third edition). Portsmouth, NH: Heinemann, 2009.

NOTES:

NOTES:

Informal Assessments for Text Comprehension

NOTES:

NOTES:

NOTES:

NOTES:

Informal Assessments for Text Comprehension